Sticker Safari
FARM
Mariana Ruiz Johnson
templar
books

Rise and Shine

When the first rays of sun rise over the fields, the cockerel crows his morning call. Cock-a-doodle-doo! Cows moo, sheep bleat and hungry shire horses whinny for their breakfast. Good morning, farm!

Who else is waking up this morning? Stick some more animals into the farmyard. Can you give them some food to eat?

Birds of a feather

The farmer drives his tractor up and down the field, ploughing the ground before he plants new crops. Behind the tractor, pink worms wriggle in the churned-up earth. Birds flock over the fields, hoping to catch a juicy worm!

How many birds can you count? Use your stickers to make the flock even bigger, then dress up the scarecrows.

Baby days

Spring on the farm brings lots of new arrivals. Lambs skip in the sunny meadows, newborn foals take their first wobbly steps and fluffy chicks chirrup in the treetops. Everywhere around them there are bright flowers and fluttering butterflies.

Someone has left the gate open! Stick in a sheepdog to round up the run-away lambs, then fill the meadow with more flowers.

How egg-citing

Outside the henhouse, chickens scratch and peck in the sunshine. Inside the cosy coop, other hens are having a snooze, sitting comfortably on their nests. How many eggs can you spot hidden in the hay?

Stick some chickens onto the empty nests. Now put in stickers to get everyone ready for chick school!

Messy mud baths

It's a rainy day and the pig field is full of happy hogs, stomping and sploshing in muddy puddles. On hot days, mud helps the pigs keep nice and cool, but these piggies love mud whatever the weather!

Put some more muddy animals into the pigsty. Use your stickers to give them colourful welly boots to wear.

Pond playtime

The farm pond is very busy today! Ducklings waddle in a line along the bank, dragonflies flit through the air and frogs croak loudly in the bulrushes. Everybody has things to do and places to be.

Can you stick in another elegant swan and give the swans some cygnets? Then add more birds, bugs and frogs.

Cutting the grass

Out in the orchard, goats graze on the grass, keeping it short and smart. Old bearded billy goats hold their heads high, showing off their long, curly horns. Meanwhile, the nanny goats rest in the shade of the fruit trees.

Stick some playful kids around the grown-up goats. Fill the trees with juicy apples and make a sticker picnic on the grass.

Milking time

Every morning and afternoon, the cows wander up to the milking shed and the farmer uses special machines to milk the herd. Beep, beep! Then the milkman drives into the yard, ready to load up his float.

Choose the stickers to fill the milk float with bottles of fresh, creamy milk. Now give the cows some cupcakes to eat.

Off to market

The shire horse waits patiently outside the farmhouse - it's time to take the farmer's goods to market. Behind the cart, bees buzz around the hive, making scrummy honey for everyone to enjoy.

Load the cart with jars of honey and strawberry jam. Use your stickers to give the horse a flowery hat!

Harvest time

Now summer has passed, the vegetable patch is bursting with fat pumpkins and the wheat field is turning golden yellow. The combine harvester works day and night to bring in the corn, and everyone is busy picking vegetables.

Can you make this year's harvest even bigger? Add more vegetables, then stick in some scampering animals!

Fiddle-dee-dee!

All the animals are crowded into the barn for the night. It's warm and dry in here, and everyone can be together. Mice scamper along the beams, cats curl up in the straw and bats hang upside down from the rafters.

It's time for a barn dance! Find some musical instruments, add in more animals, then make a farmyard band.

A TEMPLAR BOOK

First published in the UK in 2018 by Templar Publishing,
an imprint of Kings Road Publishing,
part of the Bonnier Publishing Group,
The Plaza, 535 King's Road, London, SW10 0SZ
www.bonnierpublishing.com

1 2 3 4 5 6 7 8 9 10
0418 007

ISBN 978-1-78741-071-8

Designed by Kieran Hood and Adam Allori
Edited by Ruth Symons
Written by Mandy Archer
Printed in Malaysia

Use this space for any
spare stickers to create
your own farmyard scene!

RISE AND SHINE
chicken
sheep
cow
horse
pig
sheepdog
sheep
pig
pig
sheep
cow
rabbit
donkey
horse
cat
birds
blackbirds
worms
tractor

BIRDS OF A FEATHER

bird
scarecrow
birds
bird
owl
blackbirds
tractors
blackbird
scarecrow

BABY DAYS

scarecrow
sheep
sheep
lamb
butterfly
donkey
foal
lamb
sheep
lamb

sheepdog
lamb
horse
horse
chick
horse
foal
sheep
lamb
chick
lamb
bird
butterfly
chick
chick
chick
chickens
chicks
chicken
chicks
pig
HOW EGG-CITING

MESSY MUD BATHS

chickens

chick

chick

pigs

pigs

POND PLAYTIME

fish
newt
swan
dragonfly
duck
duckling
fish
mallard
cygnet
dragonfly
frog
mallard
fish
mallard
newt
mallard
mallard
ducklings
frog
duck
cygnet
frog
frog
cygnet
tadpoles
mallard

CUTTING THE GRASS

nanny goat
kid
nanny goats

dragonfly

nanny goat

nanny goat

nanny goat

nanny goat

nanny goat

nanny goat

billy goat

nanny goat

kids

billy goat

calf

bird

calf

rabbit

cow

cow

calf

MILKING TIME

calf

cow

cat

cow

OFF TO MARKET

cat and mouse

sheepdog

bees

rooster

donkey

sheepdog

bird

birds

cat

HARVEST TIME

rabbit

rat

bird

mouse

worms

chicks

rabbit

rat

rat
cygnet
rabbits
cat
rooster
cygnet
owl
bat
sheep
rat
bat
sheep
cat
pig
rabbit
duck
chicken
FIDDLE-DEE-DEE
pigs
rat
cow
chicken
blackbird
lamb
goat